DELUXE COLOURING
& PUZZLE BOOK

The Five Mile Press

HIDDEN FRILL-NECK

How many Jackos can you find in this scene?

I found
_____
Jackos!

4

THE ADVENTURER'S CODE

Use the clues below to find out the first
rule of the adventurer's code!

 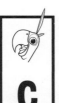

A	B	C	D	E	F	G	H	I

J	K	L	M	N	O	P	Q	R

S	T	U	V	W	X	Y	Z	!

WHO'S ODD?

Look through the pictures below
and find the odd one out.

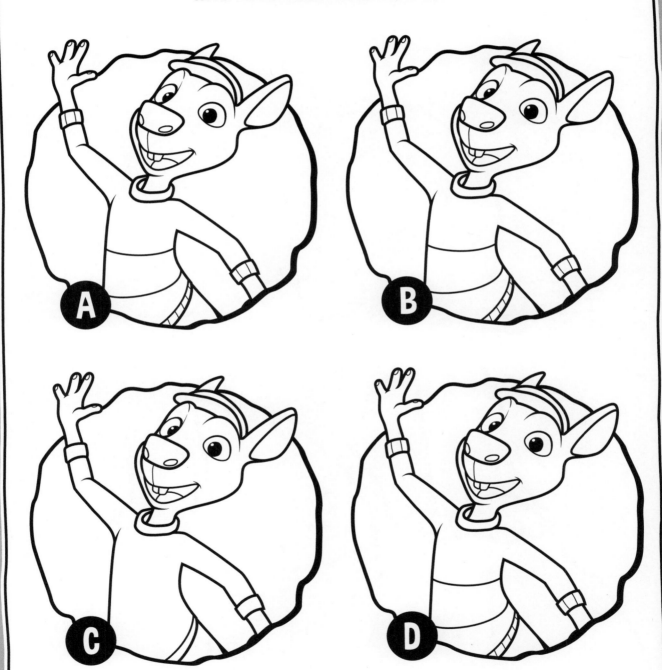

8

HOMEWARD BOUND

Blinky has found his dad and is heading home
to Greenpatch, but he has lost his way!
Help Blinky through the maze below to find home.

START →

FINISH

GREENPATCH

OUTBACK SAYINGS

Colour in these outback sayings and ask an adult to help you cut them out. Stick them up on your wall for some bonza decoration.

13

TRACKER'S CHALLENGE!

**Find all the pictures in the list.
Don't forget to tick them off as you go!**

FLYING HIGH

Blinky builds a flying machine (aka kite).
Draw you own flying machine below.
What kind of machine will it be? A fast jet plane?
A meandering hot-air balloon? You decide!

WHAT DID YOU SAY?

**Blinky and his friends are lost for words!
Fill in their speech bubbles to get them talking.
Use the phrases shown or make up your own.**

IN THE SHADOWS

Find the shadow that matches this picture of Nutsy.

The correct shadow is _____

KOALA MATCH

Use the cards below to play your own game of memory. Colour them in and ask an adult to help you cut them out.

HOW TO PLAY:

This game is great with two people, but you can also play by yourself. The aim is to match as many pairs as you can.

Lay out the cards face down. Each player turns over two cards at a time. If the cards match keep them, if they don't turn them back over. Keep taking turns until all the cards are matched.

Watch carefully and try to remember where all the cards are so you can match your pairs. The player with the most pairs wins!

BY GUMBO!

Gumnut, gumleaves ... there are so many words starting with 'gum'! Find them all in the grid below.

E	L	H	J	A	S	G	G	J	N
I	M	G	W	P	E	U	U	V	C
D	G	U	F	Q	Z	M	M	K	B
G	U	M	B	O	O	T	L	Q	T
V	M	D	P	J	C	R	E	G	H
I	W	R	D	K	Y	E	A	U	S
H	O	O	Y	B	Y	E	V	M	C
H	O	P	C	K	D	Z	E	N	X
K	D	S	A	G	I	D	S	U	C
G	U	M	B	A	L	L	R	T	P

Gumnut   Gumboot

Gumdrops   Gum tree

Gumwood   Gumball

Gumleaves

COLOUR AND CUT

Colour in these standees of your favourite *Blinky* characters. When you are done ask an adult to help you cut them out.

FOLD HERE
BLINKY

FOLD HERE
MUM & DAD

FOLD HERE
JACKO

FOLD HERE
NUTSY

FOLD HERE
WOMBO

29

BUSH BRAINIAC

**Blinky and his friends are having a race.
Nutsy is in front of Splodge; Marcia is behind Blinky;
Blinky is behind Robert; and Robert is coming third.
Who is winning the race?**

Use the space below to work out your answer.

CRAZY CREATURES

Colour in the characters on the following pages. When you are done ask an adult to help you cut along the lines. Flip the pages back and forth to create your own crazy-looking creatures!

39

44

TREE HOUSE

Blinky and his family live in a huge gum tree. If you were building a tree house what would it look like? Would you live inside the trunk? Or way up in the branches? Use the space below to draw your dream tree house.

This is Blinky's bedroom. What will yours look like?

WORDY AUSSIE

Do you know the meaning of all the Aussie words and phrases below? Write out a meaning for each word and check your answers on the answers page.

Nosh up

_____

Chocka/chockers

_____

Hooroo

_____

Give it a burl

_____

Fair dinkum!

_____

Stoked

_____

Strewth!

_____

Ridgy-didge

_____

Too right!

_____

Bonza

_____

Yonks/yonks ago

_____

Grouse

_____

ANSWERS

PAGE 3 – Hidden Frill-neck
There are 10 Jackos in the scene.

PAGE 5 – The Adventurer's Code
An adventurer never gives up.

PAGE 7 – Who's Odd?
C is the odd one out.

PAGE 9 – Homeward Bound

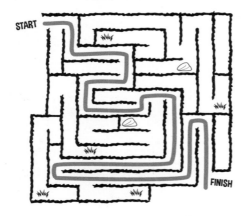

PAGES 14 & 15 – Tracker's Challenge!

PAGE 21 – In the Shadows
A is the correct shadow.

PAGE 25 – By Gumbo!

E	L	H	J	A	S	G	G	J	N
I	M	G	W	P	E	U	U	V	C
D	G	U	F	Q	Z	M	M	K	B
G	U	M	B	O	O	T	L	Q	T
V	M	D	P	J	C	R	E	G	H
I	W	R	D	K	Y	E	A	U	S
H	O	O	Y	B	Y	E	V	M	C
H	O	P	C	K	D	Z	E	N	X
K	D	S	A	G	I	D	S	U	C
G	U	M	B	A	L	L	R	T	P

PAGE 31 – Bush Brainiac
Nutsy is winning the race.

PAGE 47 – Wordy Aussie
Chocka/chockers = full
Fair dinkum! = true/genuine
Give it a burl = have a go
Grouse = great/terrific
Ridgy-didge = original/genuine
Strewth! = oh my goodness!
Stoked = very pleased
Too right! = definitely/correct
Bonza = excellent
Hooroo = goodbye
Nosh up = a good meal
Yonks, yonks ago = a long time ago